**Scotland's two hundred year old Caledonian Canal remains today as spectacular as the multicoloured ribbon of Highland scenery through which it runs. This vast working waterway is a lasting tribute to the vision and ingenuity of the great Scottish civil engineer who built it, Thomas Telford.**

**Hand-cut in the early 19th Century by rough Highland crofters, this coast to coast water highway has survived attack from construction challenges, closure campaigns, lock collapses and Westminster politicians to win through as a timeless icon heralding the start of this Millennium's New Canal Age.**

The canal has tamed the Highlands' once remote Great Glen to open up a valley of breathtaking natural beauty. It is now enjoyed by over half a million visitors every year craving the appeal of Northern Scotland's pure unspoilt environment.

This guide book tells the story of that social and engineering achievement, when proud clansmen swapped bagpipes for picks to hew out by sheer muscle over 6 million tonnes of rock and earth.

It describes how 29 massive locks, and 35km of man-made channel, have linked four of Scotland's largest freshwater lochs to create, right across the country, one of the World's first sea to sea ship canals. And it explains why it needed a dozen Victorian lock keepers, many million litres of water, and a good half day, to lift a 32 gun full-sail naval frigate some 20 metres up an impressive 'staircase' of eight linked locks – an operation that today can be achieved in just 90 minutes by simply pressing buttons.

It reveals how this impressive waterway, several times threatened with closure and abandonment, is now a major contributor to the economy of the Highlands and is recognised as a unique working example of Scotland's industrial heritage, protected by the prestigious status of a Scheduled Ancient Monument.

The canal's once forbidding remoteness, that so nearly triggered its downfall, has become instead a catalyst. Its towpaths are a mecca for walkers and cyclists. And its waters attract thousands of boat enthusiasts, both professional and amateur, plus – perhaps – just one elusive and mysterious sea creature lurking in the depths of Loch Ness.

# The Caledonian Canal
## The Making of a Scottish Monument

*Neptune's Staircase*

**The Caledonian Canal was designed not just as a shortcut between the North Sea and Atlantic Ocean. Its creation was also Britain's first foray into social engineering.**

During the late 1700s, Scotland's remote unexplored Highlands, virtually a week's carriage ride from London, were losing thousands of destitute, disillusioned clansmen every year, emigrating mainly to the appealing New World of Canada. Those who remained were starved of both employment and communications with the south. A 100km coast to coast canal, along with improvements to roads and bridges, could answer several calls.

Creation of vast stone-lined locks would offer immediate employment to crofters turned construction workers. And the canal would create a vital new route for trade, people and mail.

Its funders, the British Government, foresaw a further important benefit. Eighteenth Century sailing ships – be they fishing fleets chasing herring shoals up Scotland's shorelines, merchant boats trading with North America and the Baltic nations or naval ships at war with France – they all had to navigate round Scotland's often treacherous northern coast. The canal would offer safe haven and a shorter route.

Or so the politicians hoped: For when the project took 12 years longer to build than planned and at double the expected cost, Britain's Industrial Revolution had invaded even the Highlands. Steam power – on water and land – was to prove both the waterway's main challenge and its eventual saviour.

The canal's history has followed a roller coaster ride of decline and resurgence, unrecognisable to the pioneering men who conceived and built it.

*Corpach Basin*

**Thomas Telford, designer and builder of the Caledonian Canal, was an engineer with a mission. And he was keen to fulfil it.**

He faced an early rebuke from his boss, the Speaker of the House of Commons and Chairman of the Caledonian Canal Commissioners, by leaving for Scotland to complete a survey of the canal's route before receiving a final brief from the project's paymaster, the British Government.

He was in a hurry because this ambitious 46 year old Scottish engineer craved the challenge of constructing locks bigger than any seen before. Two were to be sited well out in tidal waters.

Others would be built in the beds of diverted rivers. Over half the total 29 locks would be linked ingeniously together into groups known as 'staircases', to lift or lower boats as much as 20 metres in the space of just a few hundred metres.

And Mr. Telford was keen also to prove he possessed the leadership skills to persuade over 1500 rough and rebellious Highlanders to build it all for him.

## Canal curios

Tomnahurick

*Highland prophet the Brahan Seer predicted, back in 1620, both the canal and its route: 'Strange as it may seem to you this day, the time will come, and it is not far off, when full-rigged ships will be seen sailing (inland) eastward and westward by the back of Tomnahurick at Inverness'.*

*Although a hard taskmaster, Mr. Telford cared for those around him. On seeing one of his workmen rescue a little girl who had fallen into the canal, he rushed up to praise him thrusting a closed purse of money into his hand. The man was amazed to find it contained gold coins valued at £11 – worth today over £800.*

*The growth of passenger steamboats brought prosperity, but angered lock keepers wives. They were ordered to take in their washing every time daytripper boats passed their canalside homes.*

# Thomas Telford – The Engineer with Vision

Leading Scottish civil engineer Thomas Telford was born in Dumfries in 1757, the only son of a shepherd. He trained as a stonemason and soon journeyed south to London to further his passion for engineering.

Lacking much formal education, his enthusiasm to learn and succeed soon singled him out from his peers. By 1803, when the government's Caledonian Canal Commission asked him to survey, design and supervise construction of Britain's most ambitious inland waterway, Mr. Telford boasted an already impressive CV.

The Menai Suspension Bridge and Pontcysyllte Aqueduct, both in Wales, headed a worthy list of bridges, harbours, churches and roads. But canals had become his specialisation, and the Caledonian was to lead a roll call of personal involvement in major waterways including the Bridgewater, Ellesmere and Shrewsbury canals.

The Caledonian dominated the next 20 years of his life, with this ingenious yet modest engineer overseeing all aspects of its construction including building techniques and even the men's wages and living accommodation. Monthly government advances for construction work were paid into his personal bank account forcing him, on occasions, to travel with saddlebags full of banknotes.

*Menai Suspension Bridge*

He designed cranes for positioning a lock wall's heavy masonry blocks and iron rail roads for horse-drawn wagons that could easily tip out their excavated material. He specified low level road bridges across the canal that would swing open sideways instead of lifting up, so tall-masted sailing ships had an easier passage.

In 1820, two years before the canal fully opened, Thomas Telford was rewarded for his engineering prowess by becoming founding President of Britain's now World-renowned Institution of Civil Engineers.

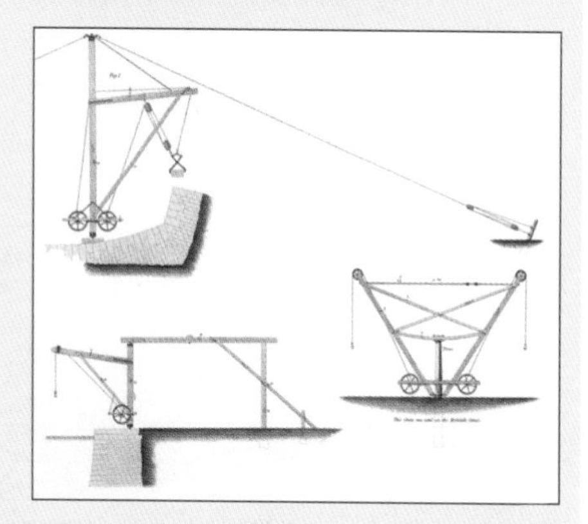

*Pontcysyllte Aqueduct*

## Cutting the Canal – with Picks, Wheelbarrows and Horses

Excavating the canal itself, 15 metres wide at the bottom and 34 metres at the top, involved gangs of up to150 men working with picks, shovels and the then unfamiliar construction tool – the wheelbarrow. It is said that development of the modern shaped wheelbarrow owes much to the navvies building the Caledonian.

The soil was 'barrowed' up the cutting's sides to waiting horse-drawn, rail-mounted wagons which moved it to areas where canal banks needed to be higher. Clever wagon designs, decades ahead of their time, included side or bottom sections that opened for easy removal of the soil.

Four separate lengths of channel were cut, totalling 35km and linking the canal's four natural lochs.

The canal was largely unlined. In some areas it was sealed with puddle clay – a light cohesive clay mixed with water before men 'puddled' or trod it into embankment cracks using their boots. In one particularly leaky area, strips of woollen matting from a nearby mill were laid out over the canal bed and covered with clay.

Had he known, as he journeyed north from London to Scotland's Great Glen early in 1803, that this monumental task would take nearly three times longer than planned – and cost double its estimated price – then perhaps his enthusiasm would have waned.

But construction delays, workforce problems and a significant shortfall in the canal's expected early customers, were all in the future. Mr. Telford thought only of designing and building the largest canal of its type anywhere.

And could he have fast-forwarded two centuries, to witness the ever growing success of today's tourist-orientated waterway, then doubtless he would have thought his early zeal well justified.

He was travelling to an isolated land, cut off from the rest of Britain, but surprisingly one more populous than it is today. The Jacobite Rebellion had been lost some 50 years earlier; leaving many Highland clans – backers of Bonnie Prince Charlie's illfated march south to capture the British throne – facing ignominious defeat.

Robbed of the right to wear the Tartan, play the bagpipes or even speak their own Gaelic tongue, these hunter-gatherers now endured further suffering – unemployment.

The so called 'Highland Clearances' centred on distant owners of the region's once widespread agricultural and cattle rearing farmsteads abandoning them in favour of more lucrative, less labour intensive sheep farming. Evicted, persecuted and out of work Highland tenants emigrated in their

## Canal curios

*The gruesome murder in 1663 of two sons of a Highland chief, butchered by the clan leader's own brothers attempting to deny the young men their inheritance, is commemorated by a bizarre seven-headed monument to the assassins. The Well of the Seven Heads, near Clunes on Loch Lochy, marks the spot where the seven murderers were rounded up and beheaded by loyal clansmen, who then washed the severed heads in the well.*

*The canal was hand-dug by over 1500 unskilled Highland farmers who were soon called navvies; the traditional name for a canal builder. Early 17th Century canals had been called navigations; so their builders were termed navvies. The Irish became the most experienced navvies, later employed building many of Britain's railways.*

*Near Laggan Locks, the 1554 'Battle of the Shirts' had a poignant epilogue when two Highland clans fought each other one hot summer's day. Both sides had discarded their shirts beforehand and, after the battle, only a handful of Highlanders remained alive on either side. As they staggered back to their camps, both groups faced massive piles of unclaimable shirts.*

thousands, either south to the Scottish Lowlands or across the Atlantic to Canada.

Mr. Telford's prime mission in building the canal was to provide instant local employment and a new communications highway. He had a further brief from government to finish the task started by General Wade 80 years earlier, and criss-cross the region with roads and bridges. He was eventually to build over 1000 bridges and 1500km of road, some linking with his new waterway.

The canal was also to offer coastal fishing fleets, transcontinental trading clippers and Britain's Navy – still waging the Napoleonic Wars – a more secure journey to work than the Northern Scottish coast's treacherous Pentland Firth and Cape Wrath. Scores of sailing ships, both civilian and military, would flounder on its treacherous rocks or be storm-bound for months.

The possibility of a canal, routed along an extensive geological fault through the Great Glen and incorporating, for two thirds of its length, four of Scotland's natural lochs – Ness, Oich, Lochy and Dochfour – had been muted as early as 1700. But its reality needed the

## Canal curios

*Look out at major lock sites for the distinctive white, bay-windowed houses built by Thomas Telford, at first for his construction managers and then lock keepers. The windows, both upstairs and down, offer excellent views right along the locks – so no excuse for the manager not attending to his duties day or night.*

*Engineers attempted to dilute the Highlanders' love of whisky by opening up a site brewery, encouraging them to swap to beer. It failed, as the clansmen merely downed both drinks together – giving rise to the expression 'taking a hauf and hauf'. They even ensured they drained every dram of whisky from their glasses by swilling them out with beer.*

*The canal's opening was celebrated in true Highland spirit with 67 dignitaries taking a two day steamship trip to one end and back again. A highlight of the nightstop banquet at Fort William was ensuring full value from their whisky by proposing an amazing 39 toasts. Praise for Mr. Telford ranked only the nineteenth, and it was reported that all dinner guests remained fit for the early morning return departure.*

combination of a government willing to pay for it – making it the only British canal to have always been publicly owned – plus the skill of Thomas Telford and his hand picked engineers who, between them, already had an impressive record of canal building.

Mr. Telford himself teamed up with his close colleague and engineering mentor William Jessop to plan an estimated seven year, £474,000 construction project. Their canal was to be built inwards, simultaneously from sea locks at Fort William in the west and Inverness near the east coast. Construction of a central section would be started later, supplied with rock and materials brought in by boat along already flooded, and hopefully completed, outer lengths of canal.

But the programme did not work out as planned, following construction delays particularly with end sections. The ground along the route proved difficult and as varied as the massive 52 metre long locks to be built in it.

At both entrances to the canal, vast 10 metre deep sea locks, with strong oak gates, were needed to hold back tidal waters. On the eastern coast, where the canal enters the Beauly Firth off Inverness, this sea lock was sited on top of mud 17 metres thick. Mr. Telford thought up an innovative solution of preloading the mud with tonnes of rock for six months to allow it to consolidate and

## The Construction Army – Hard Working, Hard Drinking

**A yearning for whisky was a major factor influencing construction workers' productivity. Farming as tenant crofters had been their main occupation and even basic construction tools such as picks were alien to them.**

**Living in turf-walled huts alongside lock sites, the men were hard workers; but only until the distant potato harvest or peat-cutting seasons beckoned them back to their crofts for several months at a time. Once there, out came the farmstead's resident whisky distilling equipment and more than a few drops of the hard stuff would delay their return to the canal site.**

**Engineers even had a brewery built on one of the larger sites to tempt the men off whisky and onto beer. But Highland traditions are not for breaking, and the weaker alcohol merely became an addition, rather than a substitute, to the men's liquid diet.**

**Despite a labourer's relatively handsome pay of a guinea (105 pence) a week –equivalent to about £76 today – absenteeism remained a problem, forcing engineers to bring in more experienced Irish workers. This triggered criticism from the Government as a main aim of the canal was to help alleviate local unemployment among the Highlanders.**

*Corpach Sealock*

## Cavernous Locks – Hand Built by Highlanders

The canal's construction workforce, peaking to over 1500 Highlanders, built 29 of the largest locks ever seen. Averaging 52 metres long and 10 metres deep, they had inverted arch-shaped bases for added strength.

Rubble filled, double-leaf masonry walls nearly 2 metres thick were formed with up to 1 metre long rectangular dressed stone blocks. The 20 tonne cast iron lock gates were brought to site in sections, by sea from English foundries, and assembled alongside their locks.

In three places locks were grouped together in 'staircases' to reduce construction time and costs. The largest group of eight locks, known as Neptune's Staircase, took over 900 men nearly four years to complete.

Over 300,000 tonnes of earth and stone had to be excavated to create all the 29 locks – sufficient to create a pile of rock 25 metres high if spread over a full-sized football pitch.

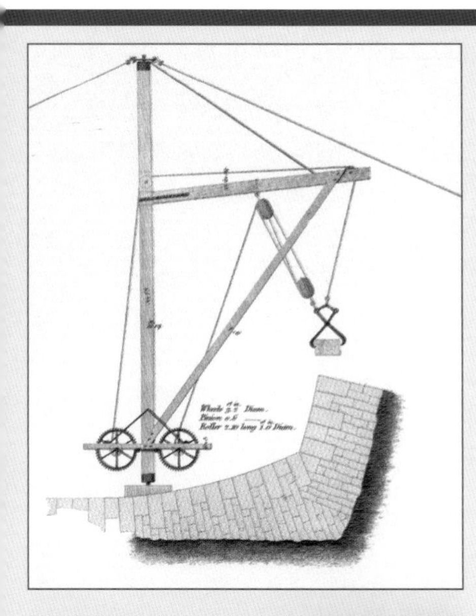

Collapse at Corpach Double Lock

settle before building the lock on its then firmer foundations.

Some 100km to the south west, the equivalent sea lock at Corpach near Fort William sat conveniently on solid rock. But in between, locks were built in the gravel beds of diverted rivers or alongside deep natural lochs where large steam-powered water pumps worked round the clock to keep excavations dry.

In three places, Fort William, Fort Augustus and at Inverness, locks were, for the first time in Scotland, linked together to create staircases up to eight high. This allowed boats to be raised or lowered by up to 20 metres in a single 500 metre long section.

Delays and construction costs escalated such that the revelry of the 1822 canal opening celebrations could not totally erase the realisation that they were occurring 12 years later than originally planned. And the distant British Government in London faced a final bill of over £900,000 - twice original estimates and swelled largely by a near doubling in the costs of labourers wages, food and building materials.

The delay was to result in the waterway's intended main customers outgrowing its advantages. The canal had been excavated to a depth of less than 4.5 metres – just three quarters the draft planned in 1803. These shallower waters, and rapid growth of larger steam-powered boats, meant many could not now use the canal.

The more powerful naval and cargo ships found the northern coastal route less of a challenge. With Napoleon defeated at Waterloo 7 years earlier, the British Navy no longer needed the shelter offered by the canal.

Fort Augustus

## The Invasion of Fort Augustus

Fort Augustus, on the shores of Loch Ness, was once a small cluster of cottages nestling beneath an early 18th Century military fort. It now boasts over 300,000 visitors a year, fascinated by the five interconnected canal locks that dominate the centre of the village.

This community epitomises several along the route, transformed first by its canal construction and now by seasonal invasions of boat enthusiasts and curious visitors.

Originally known as Kilcumein, until the building of a government fort changed its name in 1715, the village's real invasion came exactly a century later when an army of 300 construction workers set up their own encampment of turf-walled huts in the village centre.

This mixed bunch of Highland labourers, blacksmiths, carpenters and quarrymen were to remain for over four years while the River Oich was diverted outside the village and complex, troublesome lock construction – some of it in the old river bed – dominated community life.

Excavating tools and building materials arrived by boat at the loch jetty. Baltic timber was shipped in via Aberdeen harbour. A horse-drawn tramway was laid along the line of the new locks to import stone from a nearby quarry; and regular supplies of oatmeal, bannocks and brose – a salt flavoured porridge – formed the men's staple diet.

The base of the lowest lock lay 7 metres below the level of adjacent Loch Ness and a large steam pump took up residence in the excavation attempting to keep it dry. It consumed over one and a quarter barrels of coal every hour to pump out eight 'hogsheads' of water at every stroke.

But this wasn't enough to keep the water out, and two more steam engines joined it to add more smoke and noise round the clock. Once a month, on pay day, even the clatter of steam pumps was drowned out by revelling workers at the village pub, the only hostelry for miles around.

With the 300 metre run of completed locks, bang in the village centre, raising or lowering boats by 12 metres, Fort Augustus soon became a mecca for local trade and passenger steamboats. Its prosperity continues and a look in the canal's main information centre, alongside the lock staircase, will remind today's visitors of the backbreaking efforts needed to create their tourist attraction.

# The Great Glen's Coast to Coast Canal

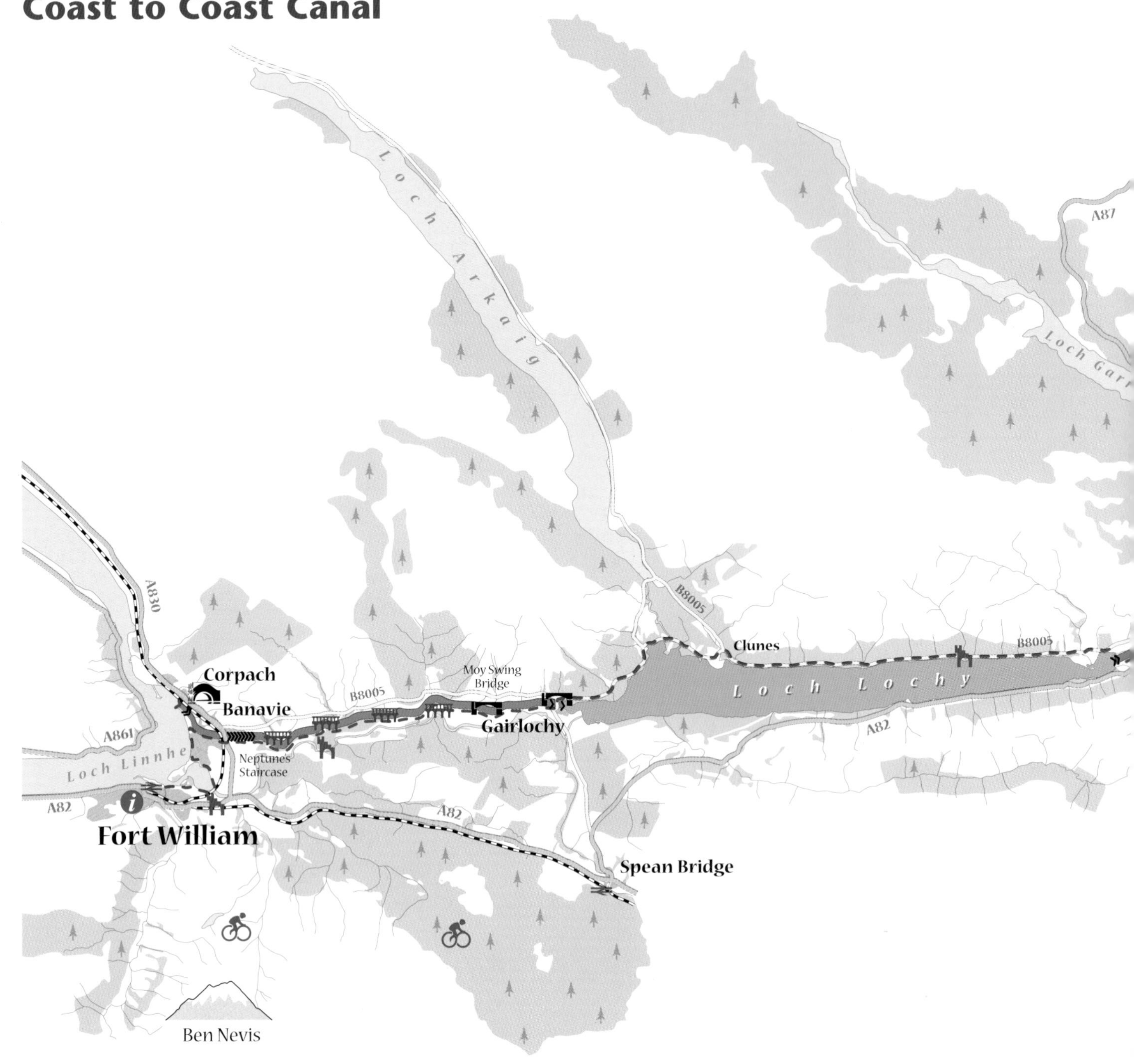

Within a few years, locks were suffering from the use of weak building materials. When one partially collapsed, it triggered the memorable description from a canal toll collector of being in an 'execrable' condition.

In 1843 the canal closed for four years to undergo major repairs and at last be deepened to a more respectable 5.5 metres. But on reopening, it recaptured only a proportion of the hoped for traffic.

A once lucrative timber trade, through the canal from Baltic ports, had waned in favour of cheaper Canadian imports. Fishing fleets were still regular customers, as was the passage of oatmeal, coal, wool and grain.

The First World War brought a boost in traffic when the Americans set up a mine assembly base at Inverness, with components shipped through the locks from the United States. But the canal never really achieved commercial success despite maintaining, for several years, cargo toll charges of just a farthing (0.1 pence) per ton per mile.

There were repeated calls for its closure – notably following the expensive disruption of ship collisions with lock gates or the partial collapse of masonry walls. The decisive crunch point came in the early 1990s when leaking and bulging lock walls signalled the need for virtually all to be rebuilt and their gates replaced.

Government made it plain to British Waterways, which had taken ownership of virtually all UK canals in 1962, that the estimated £60 million rebuild price tag was simply not available. So instead engineers devised and undertook an ingenious repair plan at a third of the cost.

By adapting age-old materials for use with 21st Century repair techniques, British Waterways has now safeguarded the canal infrastructure for at least the next 100 years. And it's future looks healthier and more vibrant than ever.

## Timeline – From Prophesy to Rescue

**1620** Canal predicted by Brahan Seer prophet Kenneth MacKenzie
**1746** The Jacobite army, including Highlanders, defeated by Government forces at Culloden
**1773** First survey of canal route by James Watt
**1803** Canal construction starts at both ends following survey by Thomas Telford
**1811** Work starts on central canal section
**1815** Napoleonic Wars end with Wellington's victory over French at Waterloo
**1818** Eastern section of canal from Inverness to Fort Augustus opens for navigation
**1822** Full length of canal opens – 12 years later than first estimated
**1843/47** Canal closed for major repairs
**1920** Caledonian Canal Commissioners hand over ownership to the Ministry of Transport
**1934** Famous first photograph of the Loch Ness Monster
**1962** British Waterways takes over canal ownership
**1964/69** Locks mechanised
**1995/2005** Major repairs and lock gate replacement safeguards canal for at least 100 years

# The Canal of Locks and Lochs

**The Caledonian Canal was intended to be a working waterway for 19th Century trade, but it failed to generate sufficient traffic to trigger commercial success. This, ironically, is part of the reason why it has survived for two centuries to now attract a very different type of customer.**

In contrast to most Victorian canals with their industrial architecture, the Caledonian's appeal became its untouched stunning and dramatic scenery, with not a factory or warehouse in sight.

The other reason for its new found popularity was Queen Victoria. Long before the word 'tourist' was invented, our very correct Queen Vic became one of the canal's early and most influential daytrippers.

Her much publicised 1873 outing along the canal signalled approval for families in their thousands to take the pure Highland air while travelling on an already growing armada of pleasure steamboats offering daytrips.

Another form of steampower, the railways, would later become the canal's main rival. But early rail routes to Fort William, Fort Augustus or Inverness offered timetables that linked with pleasureboat services, further boosting canal visitors.

Today, the continuing lack of industry, both on and alongside the canal, is the prime catalyst in attracting over half a million annual tourists to its waters or towpath. The canal has become one of the region's most successful enterprises, contributing significantly to the Highlands' economy.

Visitors marvel at the contrasting, yet always spectacular, scenery. Man-made canal sections, featuring cavernous staircases of locks, offer the excitement of swirling water with busy lock keepers weaving between curious sightseers.

Away from the locks – the exact opposite. Tranquil waters idle through a collage of countryside colour against the backdrop of forest and mountain scenery as dramatic as any in Europe.

## Canal curios

*The Caledonian is twinned with both Sweden's Götta Kanal and Canada's Rideau Canal. While still building the Caledonian, Thomas Telford helped design the Götta; a very similar ship canal with locks and lakes stretching along its 190km route between the Baltic and the North Sea. Mr. Telford had no direct involvement with the similar era 200km Rideau Canal, linking Ottawa with Kingston on Lake Ontario. But this too mirrored the infrastructure and purpose of the Caledonian, especially its scenery and later recreational use.*

*Who is the fittest of the canal's 60 strong team of lock keepers, engineers and maintenance crews? The lock keepers who man Fort William's eight lock Neptune's Staircase. On a busy day they have to repeatedly walk up and down their patch covering at least 15km. Maintenance men, who regularly mow over 8km of canalside grass in a single session, come a close second.*

*When a canal basin was drained for repairs, among the usual number of old iron bedsteads, supermarket trolleys and traffic cones found on the bottom, were four cars - including the ubiquitous Ford Anglia - and a red phone box; standing upright ready for use.*

## Water Supply – Frequent, Fresh and Free

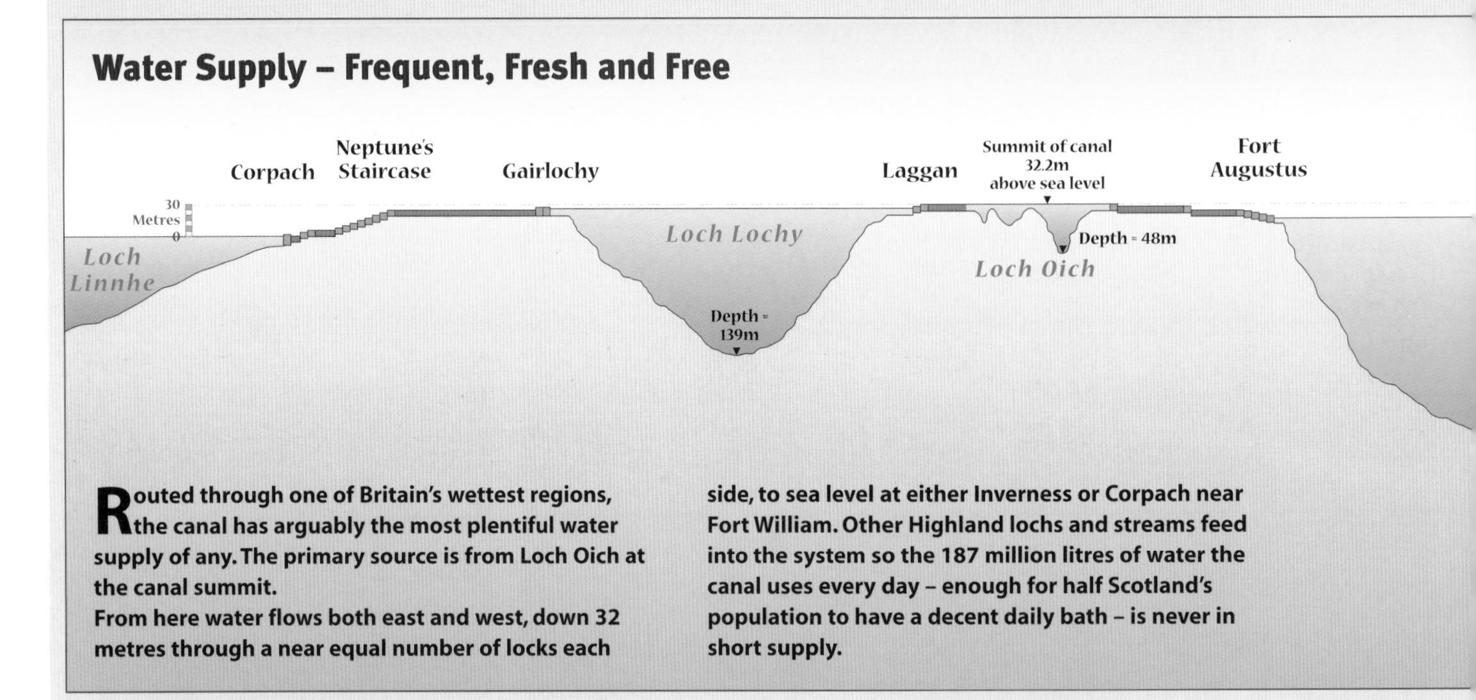


**Routed through one of Britain's wettest regions, the canal has arguably the most plentiful water supply of any. The primary source is from Loch Oich at the canal summit.**
**From here water flows both east and west, down 32 metres through a near equal number of locks each side, to sea level at either Inverness or Corpach near Fort William. Other Highland lochs and streams feed into the system so the 187 million litres of water the canal uses every day – enough for half Scotland's population to have a decent daily bath – is never in short supply.**

Adding to the 'wow' factor, the narrow cut channel suddenly metamorphoses into the vast, exposed environment of a freshwater Scottish loch. Four of them help form the canal route - from the smallest Loch Dochfour, barely 2km long, to the awe inspiring Loch Ness.

This is Scotland's largest loch; deep enough to envelope two Forth Rail Bridges on top of each other. Its 35km stretch of water occupies sufficient volume to house the World's population three times over – plus, perhaps, just one sea monster.

Passage through these lochs offers the contrast of suddenly facing exhilarating Highland air and being surrounded by steep-sided mountains that seem to slip silently beneath dark unexplored waters.

Loch Locky

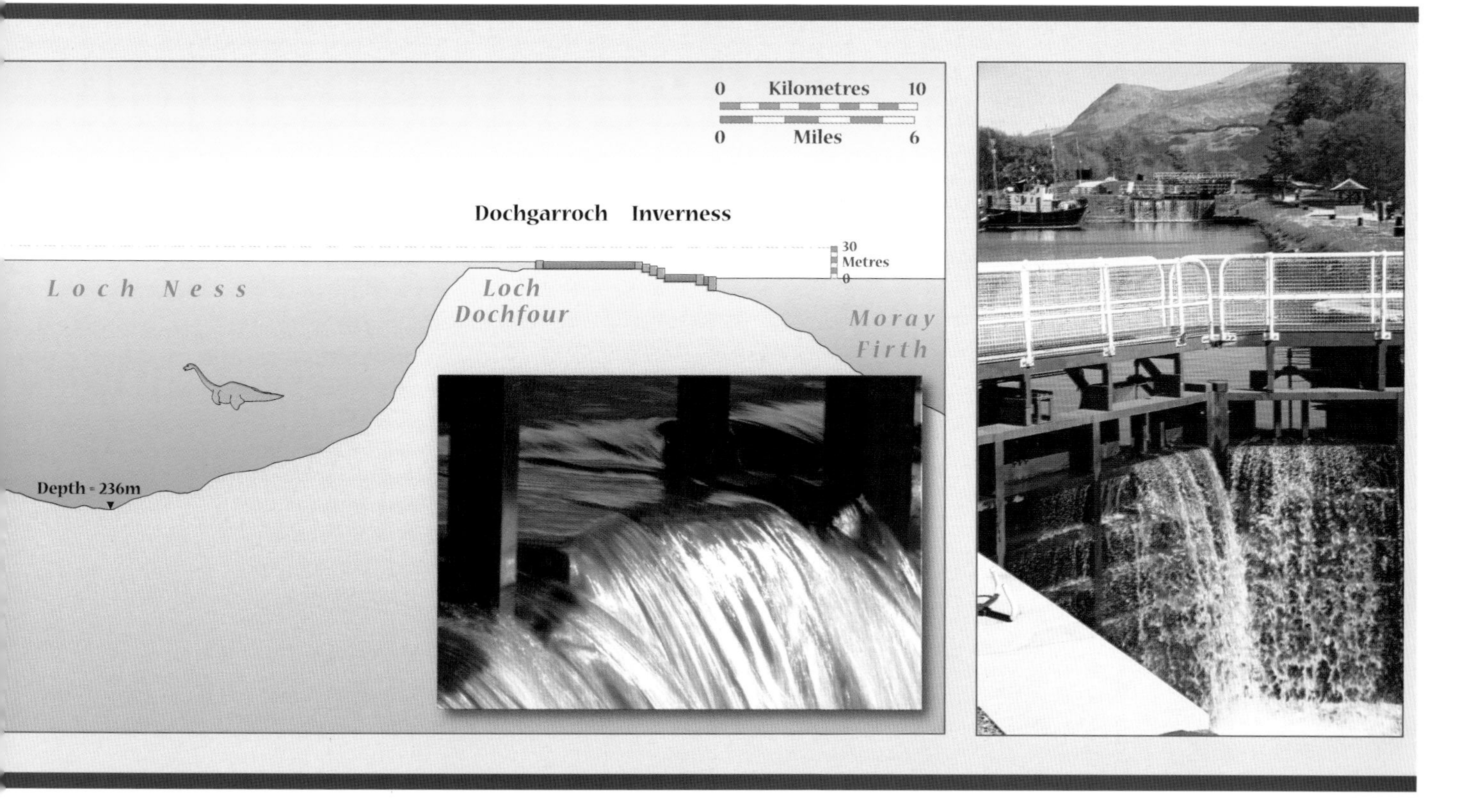

Fort Augustus Staircase

Today up to 2000 boats, flying the flags of a dozen countries, enjoy this experience every year. They range from ocean-going yachts, naval torpedo boats and full-masted reproduction 18th Century sailing ships, to smaller pleasure craft, two man dinghies and even the odd – very odd – amphibious car.

Their crews experience one of the most innovative and exciting inland waterways anywhere. From their port holes or decks they will see Britain's highest mountain, the 1344 metre snow-capped Ben Nevis.

They will witness their boats being raised up 20 metres through an eight lock 500 metre long continuous mass of masonry. And they will sail past some half dozen castles or forts; a reminder of the region's rebellious, barbarian past boasting local battles and national wars.

The canal's three main communities display a lasting commitment to that history. They once represented a defensive line across

## Lock Staircases – Saving Time and Water

**The canal's three sets of 'staircase' locks were the first of their type in Scotland. Ingenious yet simple, they save time, water and cost as they raise or lower boats as much as 20 metres through a linked group of up to eight locks.**

**Each stage, or 'locking', uses some 1.4 million litres of water – a relatively small volume compared to the near limitless supply of Highland rain feeding the canal.**

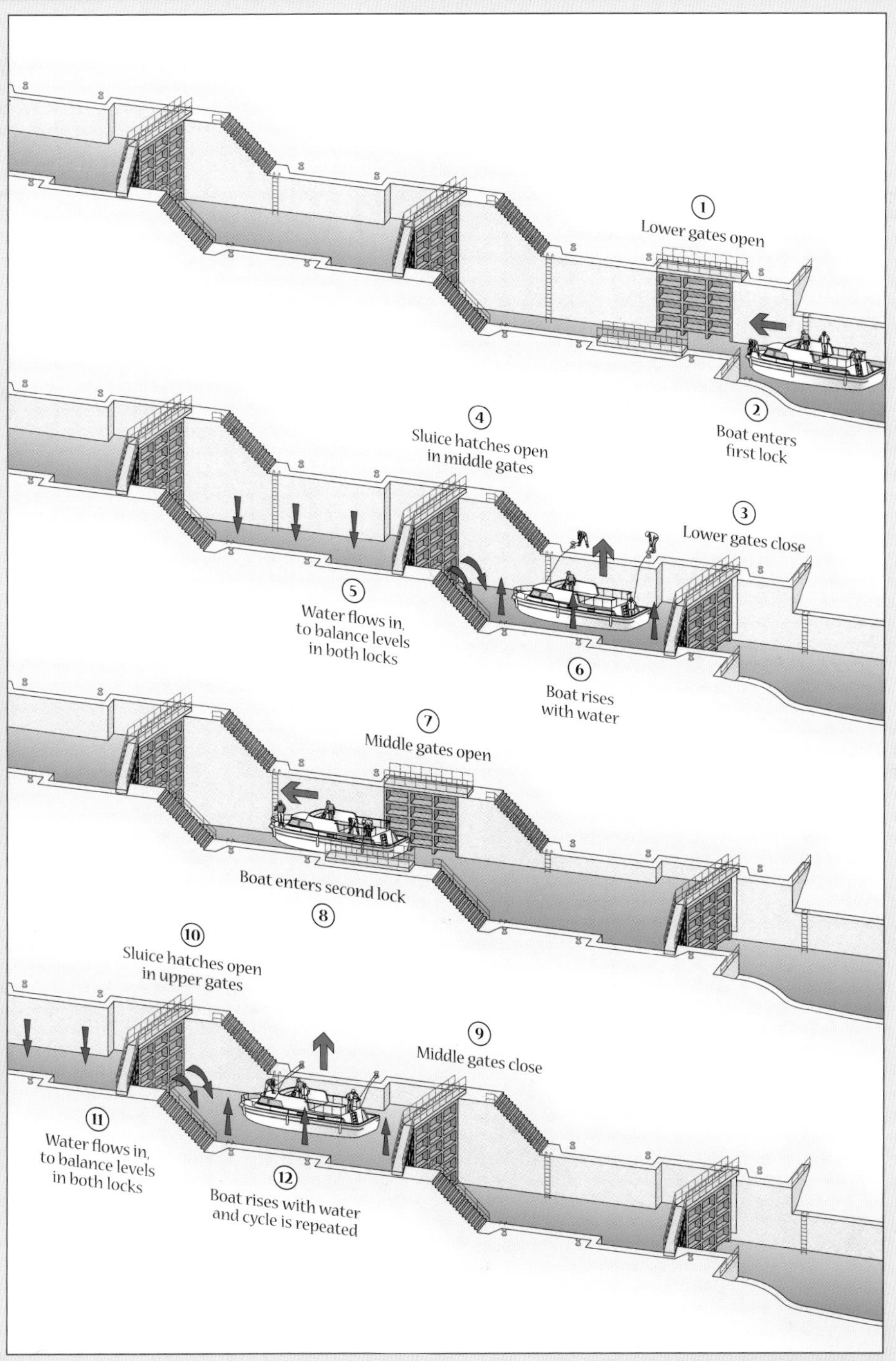

1
Lower gates open
2
Boat enters
first lock
4
Sluice hatches open
in middle gates
3
Lower gates close
5
Water flows in,
to balance levels
in both locks
6
Boat rises
with water
7
Middle gates open
Boat enters second lock
8
10
Sluice hatches open
in upper gates
9
Middle gates close
11
Water flows in,
to balance levels
in both locks
12
Boat rises with water
and cycle is repeated

Large Vessels
Operating
14 Titanic
130547 S

British Waterways Scotland
Thank you for using The Caledonian Canal
We hope you enjoyed The Great Glen
Bon voyage!

Scotland's against invading forces, notably the 18th Century Jacobite Rebellion led by Bonnie Prince Charlie.

At the canal's western end, Fort William, in the shadow of Ben Nevis, marked the site of a 1654 British Government fort named after King William III. It lasted two centuries before being demolished for an 1890 railway station. Today the town is a popular tourist centre despite claiming some of the highest rainfall figures in Britain.

Half way along the canal, some 50km north east, Fort Augustus gave its name to another government fort, captured in 1746 by the Jacobite army. When the fort was abandoned 76 years later, its contents were shipped out along the just opened canal which by then had converted the village centre into a staircase of five locks. Today, with the canal's main visitor centre alongside, these locks are the region's top free tourist attraction.

At the canal's eastern exit into the Beauly Firth stands the Highlands' capital Inverness. It boasts a castle rather than a fort, and a comparatively new 1834 one at that. But not far away is Fort George, built after the

**Fort Augustus**

## Canal curios

***Moy Bridge near Gairlochy is the only remaining original cast iron twin-leaf swing bridge among the canal's eight road and two rail crossings. It is still hand operated by the bridge keeper who, after opening one side, must boat across the canal to open the other half.***
***It provides access to only a few local farms, but remains bound by its original 1820s agreement to always be operational. Sadly the traditional red coloured rowing boat has now been replaced by a less appealing rubber dinghy with outboard motor.***

# Opening the Gates – From Capstans to Buttons

Lock gates on most canals are operated manually, using long balance beams attached to them. The Caledonian's massive 20 tonne gates were originally also hand operated by a complex network of capstans, chains and manpower.

A capstan is essentially a long vertical turning screw arrangement with a chain attached to its lower end, alongside the bottom of the lock. The chain's other end was fixed to one of the gate's two opening leaves. This allowed the turning capstan to wind in the chain, so opening or closing half the gate.

Two capstans were needed to operate each half gate. One – on the side of the lock nearest the gate leaf – would wind it open: Another, on the opposite side, would wind it closed.

Each capstan had four horizontal poles acting as arms and had to be turned seven times to complete a gate opening or closing cycle. Fort William's eight lock Neptune's Staircase needed 36 capstans to be turned a total 126 times; taking a good half day to move a boat up or down the flight. It is estimated that to manoeuvre a boat right through the canal needed a total of 1176 'turns of the capstan'.

The locks were fully mechanised by 1969 and today the equivalent button-pushing operation takes just 90 minutes, with the gates controlled by hydraulically powered rams.

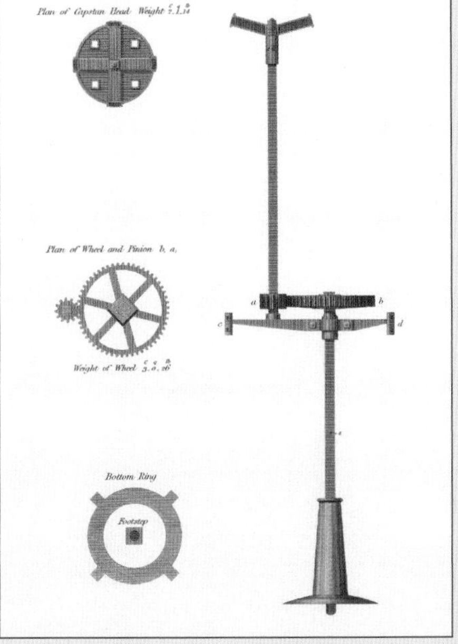

# The Environmental Valley – a Linear Oasis

The steep-sided 180km long Great Glen Valley acts like a linear wildlife oasis attracting such a wide mix of birds, plants, insects and animals that even the least attentive daytripper would find it difficult not to see something that generates a 'wow' factor.

The area features six protected wildlife sites of Special Scientific Interest while the water in its canal and rivers is some of the most unpolluted in Britain. Ironically it is this highest category water quality that contributes to a distinct lack of one wildlife species – fish.

So pure is the water that even the lowest food chain nutrients are scarce, leading to a consequential reduction in life-sustaining fish food. Surveys suggest there are 200 times less fish in the waterway than in the Scottish Lowlands Forth & Clyde Canal. The area does though boast a world-threatened eel-like fish called Lamprey.

This underwater shortfall is more than compensated for by an abundance of life in canal banks and forested valley. Ospreys, herons, buzzards and eagles contrast with water-skimming Daubenton bats, Red squirrel and even wildcats.

Otters can be seen basking by lock gates, while Northern Marsh Orchid and the fernlike Quillwort head up over 200 varieties of plant life. And to go home boasting of seeing the obscure 'Bolitophagus Reticulates' insect would certainly give you lots of countryside credibility.

Ben Nevis

Jacobites' 1746 defeat at nearby Culloden.

With so much to see alongside the canal, it is not surprising that it attracts even more boots than boats. Every year over 10,000 walkers enjoy sections of the Great Glen Way; a 120km waymarked footpath, a third of which is routed along the towpath.

Bikes make up the transport trilogy, with mountain bike trails following a similar route to the Great Glen Way and featuring five off-road forest sections for enthusiasts.

## Canal curios

*Among the more unusual vessels using the canal have been an amphibious Land Rover, a tin whale, a rowing boat journeying between Norway and Dublin plus - it was rumoured back in the 1820s - a shy young sea monster on route from the Scandinavian Arctic to Loch Ness.*

## The Loch Ness Mystery – Myth or Monster

**A television monitor, sited in the bar of the Loch Ness pleasure steamer Jacobite Queen, relays a moving, three dimensional sonar image of the loch bed as the boat makes its twice daily outings. "Keep a look out for the monster" the steamer's captain tells passengers "and have your cameras ready as we approach its most likely home near Urquhart Castle".**

**The captain's white beard conceals a wry smile though, in a lowered voice, he admits that he too did see something unexplainable one calm evening. His possible sighting of the Highlands' most infamous, elusive, controversial and crowd-pulling attraction – the Loch Ness Monster – adds to the 1000 plus similar reported encounters since St. Columba allegedly saw 'a horrible great Scottish beastie' crossing the loch in AD565.**

**Following the first modernday sighting in 1868, locals, holidaymakers, professional naturalists, international television crews, devoted Nessie hunters and even a 24 boat flotilla armed with the latest sonar equipment, have all witnessed or recorded the movements of a strange sea monster.**

No one has really proved anything. No one has any tangible evidence. Yet a remarkable number of the sightings describe virtually the same profile of a thin-necked creature with a humped back. This is translated, by experts having a best guess, into a 5 metre long prehistoric plesiosaw-like warm blooded reptile.

Bar a few notorious hoaxes, most observers believe resolutely that what they saw was indeed some unknown sea creature. Britain's largest single volume of freshwater, deeper in places than the North Sea, is certainly capable of concealing something as yet undiscovered by man.

In 1981, a Nessie hunt using sonar did discover a population of Arctic Char, one of Britain's rarest fish which have been living undetected deep in the loch for over 12,000 years.

Who then can say that a reptilian-like creature, a survivor from a much earlier age, could not also be swimming among the char in these deep unexplored waters? And who would even want to?

Sonar was used in Loch Ness to locate a previously forgotten 1940s Wellington bomber which had ditched in the loch. It was lifted to the surface in 1985 and is now fully restored and on display at Brooklands Aircraft Museum, Weybridge, Surrey.

Coordinating this wide ranging tourist appeal is the Great Glen Ways Initiative, a partnership between British Waterways, Highland Council and Scotland's Forestry Commission. The group offers advice and provides information boards located right through the valley; appealing especially to visitors arriving by 'boot, bike or boat'.

Tranquil yet wild; remote yet spectacular – The Caledonian Canal is any of these to all its visitors. Owner British Waterways hopes to double visitor numbers to over a million by 2012. If it succeeds none of these accolades will change.

For this vast expanse of Scottish Highlands is the one place that visitors can only enhance rather than invade.

And this fascinating waterway of locks and lochs, which Queen Victoria described as 'a masterpiece of engineering', will long provide the most appropriate gateway to some of Britain's most beautiful, unspoilt scenery.

## Canal curios

'Funny, it's just not how I ever imagined it!'

*As an act of friendship with the Caledonian twinned Götta Kanal, British Waterways' bosses have presented its Swedish owners with one of the Loch Ness Monster's massive eggs. The bright green egg was washed up on the shores of Loch Ness and ultrasound tests confirm it contains a living creature.*
*With much publicity, the egg was placed deep in one of Götta's lakes. Swedish monster watchers are now eagerly awaiting the birth; and any resemblance to an ostrich will be regarded as purely coincidental.*

## And finally for real canal buffs - the facts in the units of the day:

- Overall canal 60 miles long, with 22 miles of man-made channel and the rest formed by four Scottish lochs.
- Originally 11 low-level opening bridges. One was demolished in the 1960s so now eight road and two rail bridges.
- 29 locks, mainly 170ft long by 40ft wide and 32ft deep, each raising boats an average 8ft.
- Three lock 'staircases' of four, five and eight locks.
- Four small aqueducts allowing rivers to pass beneath.
- Canal rises 106ft to Loch Oich and uses 41 million gallons of water a day.
- Construction costs rose from £474,000 to £912,000.
- Construction time increased from seven years to 19.
- Takes two days to sail comfortably from end to end; though can be achieved in 14 hours.